Three Billy Goats

Retold by Sue Arengo
Illustrated by Caroline Anstey

OXFORD

UNIVERSITY PRESS

Before you read, can you match the words with the pictures?

1 big goat

2 little goat

3 grass

4 very big goat

5 bridge

6 troll

7 river

THERE are three goats.
There's a little goat.
There's a big goat.
And there's a very big goat.

goat

The three goats like grass.
'I'm hungry!' says the very big black goat.

'I'm **very** hungry!' says the big red goat.

grass   He's **hungry**

The three goats see a river.
They see green, green grass.
'Look!' says the little goat.
'Look at the grass!'

Look at the grass!

river

The three goats see a bridge.

But there's a troll under the bridge.
He's a bad troll.
'This is my bridge!' says the troll.

bridge   troll

The three goats see the troll.
'Look!' says the big red goat.
'There's a troll!'

Look, there's a troll!

Match the words to the pictures.

1   a happy goat

a ✓   b ☐   c ☐

2   a hungry troll

a ☐   b ☐   c ☐

3   a very big cat

a ☐   b ☐   c ☐

4   a little dog

a ☐   b ☐   c ☐

5   a bad boy

a ☐   b ☐   c ☐

Answer the questions.

1   The big goat is ...

a ☐ black   b ☑ red   c ☐ white

2   The very big goat is ...

a ☐ black   b ☐ red   c ☐ white

3   What do the goats like?

a ☐ coffee   b ☐ eggs   c ☐ grass

4   The goats are very ...

a ☐ happy   b ☐ hungry   c ☐ angry

5   The troll is under a ...

a ☐ bed   b ☐ bridge   c ☐ tree

6   He's a ... troll

a ☐ good   b ☐ happy   c ☐ bad

The three goats are very hungry.
They want the grass.
They want the green, green grass.

Tip! Tap!

The little goat goes on to the bridge.
'Tip! Tap!' go his feet.

feet

The troll hears the little goat.
'Who's on my bridge?' he says.
'It's me,' says the little goat.
'I want to eat the grass.'
The troll is hungry.
'Come here!' he says.
'I want to eat **you**.'

eat

'Please don't eat me!' says the little goat.
'I'm little.
Wait for the next goat.
He's big.'
The troll listens. The troll thinks.
'OK,' says the troll.
And the little goat goes over the bridge.

The big goat goes on to the bridge.
'Tip! tap!' go his feet.

The troll hears the big goat.
'Who's on my bridge?' he says.
'It's me,' says the big goat.
'I want to eat the grass.'

What do they say?

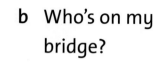

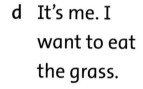

a   OK.

b   Who's on my bridge?

c   Please don't eat me! I'm little.

d   It's me. I want to eat the grass.

e   Come here! I want to eat you.

f   Wait for the next goat. He's big.

Write the words.

bridge   eat

~~goat~~   feet

grass   hungry

river   troll

1 tgao

_g o a t_   _ _ _ _ _ _

2 rigedb

3 teef

_ _ _ _

4 rllto

_ _ _ _ _

5 i e r v r

_ _ _ _ _

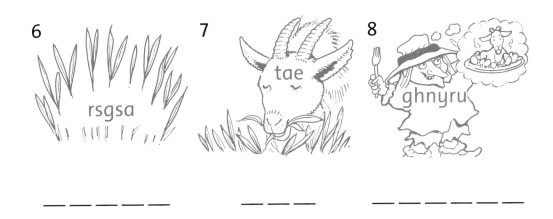

6 rsgsa

_ _ _ _ _

7 tae

_ _ _

8 ghnyru

_ _ _ _ _ _

The troll is hungry.

'Come here!' he says.

'I want to eat **you**.'

'Please don't eat me!' says the big goat.
'Wait for the next goat.
He's very big.'
The troll listens. The troll thinks.
'OK,' says the troll.
And the big goat goes over the bridge.

The very big goat goes on to the bridge.
'Tip! Tap!' go his feet.
The troll hears the very big goat.
'Who's on my bridge?' he says.
'It's me,' says the very big goat.

'I'm hungry,' says the very big goat.
'I want to eat the grass.'
But the troll's hungry.
'Come here!' he says.
'I want to eat **you**!'

Answer the questions.

1 Is he red?
   <u>No, he isn't.</u>

2 Is he little?
   _____

3 Is he little?
   _____

4 Is he black?
   _____

5 Is he red?
   _____

6 Is he very big?
   _____

18

Put the words in the correct order.

1   very   goats   hungry.   The   are

    The goats are very hungry.

2   bridge.   They   to   on   a   go

_____

3   want   grass.   eat   to   They   the

_____

4   to   The   troll   eat   the   wants   goats.

_____

5   big   goes   the   over   bridge.   goat   The

_____

6   goat.   hears   the   big   troll   very   The

_____

'OK. Here I come!' says the very big goat.
He runs at the troll.
'Tip! Tap! **Tip! Tap!**' go his feet.

The very big goat runs at the troll.
He hits him.

hit   run

Up goes the troll.
Up goes the bad troll.
Up, up, up.
'Help!' he says.

Down comes the troll.
Down comes the bad troll.
Down, down, down.
'Help!' he says.

And the very big goat
goes over the bridge.

The bad troll goes away.
He doesn't come back.
'Goodbye, troll!' the goats say.

The three goats eat the grass.
They eat the green, green grass.
They're happy.

Match the pictures to the sentences.

1

2

3

4

5

6

7

a 'Come here!' says the troll.

b The troll wants to eat him.

c The black goat goes on to the bridge.

d There's a troll under the bridge.

e He runs at the troll and he hits him.

f The black goat goes over the bridge.

g 'OK. Here I come!' says the black goat.

Crossword.

~~bridge~~   eat   goodbye   grass

happy   hit   hungry   over   please   see   river

3▸

5▸

7▸ ..., troll!

10▸

6▸ '... don't eat me!'

Across / Down numbered grid:
1 b r i d g e
5
6
7
8
9
10

1▾

8▾

3▾

9▾

2▾ The goats ... a river

4▾

Act the play.

Scene 1

Very big goat	I'm hungry.
Big goat	I'm **very** hungry.
Chant	They're hungry.
	They're **very** hungry.

Scene 2

Little goat	Look! Look at the grass.
Very big goat	It's green.
Big goat	It's **very** green.
Troll	This is my bridge.
Chant	The grass is green.
	It's **very** green.

Scene 3

Big goat	Look! There's a troll.
Little goat	I want the grass.
	I'm going on to the bridge.
Chant	Tip! Tap! Tip! Tap!
	He's on the bridge.

Scene 4

Troll	Who's on my bridge?
Little goat	It's me. I want to eat the grass.
Troll	Come here! I want to eat **you**.
Little goat	Please don't eat me! I'm little.
	Wait for the next goat.
	He's big.
Chant	The troll listens. The troll thinks.
Troll	OK.

Scene 5

Troll	Who's on my bridge?
Big goat	It's me. I want to eat the grass.
Troll	Come here! I want to eat **you**.
Big goat	Please don't eat me!
	Wait for the next goat.
	He's **very** big.
Chant	The troll listens. The troll thinks.
Troll	OK.

Scene 6

Chant	Tip! Tap! Tip! Tap!
	He's on the bridge.
Troll	Who's on my bridge?
Very big goat	It's me. I'm hungry.
	I want to eat the grass.
Troll	Come here!
	I want to eat **you**.
Very big goat	OK. Here I come!
Chant	Tip! Tap! Tip! Tap!
Troll	Help! Help!

Scene 7

Troll	Help! Help!
Little goat	Goodbye, troll.
Big goat	Goodbye, troll.
Very big goat	Goodbye, troll.
Chant	They're not hungry.
	The grass is green.
	The grass is **very** green.

OXFORD
UNIVERSITY PRESS

Great Clarendon Street, Oxford OX2 6DP

Oxford University Press is a department of the University of Oxford.
It furthers the University's objective of excellence in research, scholarship,
and education by publishing worldwide in

Oxford New York

Auckland Cape Town Dar es Salaam Hong Kong Karachi
Kuala Lumpur Madrid Melbourne Mexico City Nairobi
New Delhi Shanghai Taipei Toronto

With offices in

Argentina Austria Brazil Chile Czech Republic France Greece
Guatemala Hungary Italy Japan Poland Portugal Singapore
South Korea Switzerland Thailand Turkey Ukraine Vietnam

OXFORD and OXFORD ENGLISH are registered trade marks of
Oxford University Press in the UK and in certain other countries

ISBN: 978 0 19 4802529

Printed in China

This book is printed on paper from certified and well-managed sources.

ACKNOWLEDGEMENTS

Original story retold by: Sue Arengo
Illustrated by: Caroline Anstey